D1482310

Joseph TURRIN
(*1947)

CAPRICE

(1972)

for B♭ or C Trumpet and Piano

Duration/durée/Dauer: 5'10"

This work is in all its parts protected by copyright. Any utilisation without permission given by the publisher is illegal. This includes in particular copying, translations, microfilming, storage in and processing with electronic systems.

Cet ouvrage est intégralement protégé par les droits d'auteur.
Toute utilisation sans autorisation de l'éditeur est interdite, ceci en particulier en ce qui concerne la photocopie, les traductions, le microfichage et l'enregistrement dans et le traitement par les systèmes électroniques.

Das Werk ist in allen seinen Teilen urheberrechtlich geschützt.
Jede Verwertung ist ohne Zustimmung des Verlages unzulässig. Das gilt insbesondere für Vervielfältigung, Übersetzung, Mikroverfilmung, Einspeicherung in und Verarbeitung durch elektronische Systeme.

The Brass Press

a division of

Editions ● Bim

P.O. BOX 300 - CH-1674 VUARMARENS / SWITZERLAND
© ++41 (0)21 909 10 00 - Fax ++41 (0)21 909 10 09
email: order@editions-bim.com - http://www.editions-bim.com

Written for Derek Smith

CAPRICE
for B♭ or C Trumpet and Piano (1972 - 5'10")

Joseph TURRIN (*1947)

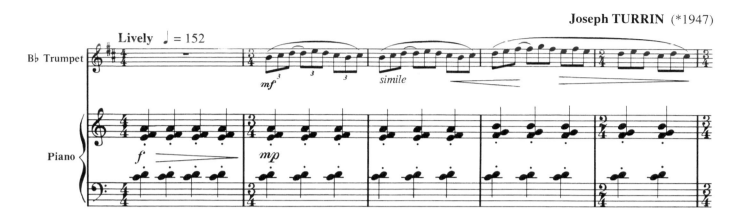

BrP TP190

@1978 World Copyright by The Brass Press / Editions Bim (Jean-Pierre Mathez), CH-1674 Vuarmarens, Switzerland
TOUS DROITS RESERVES - ALL RIGHTS RESERVED - ALLE RECHTE VORBEHALTEN

2

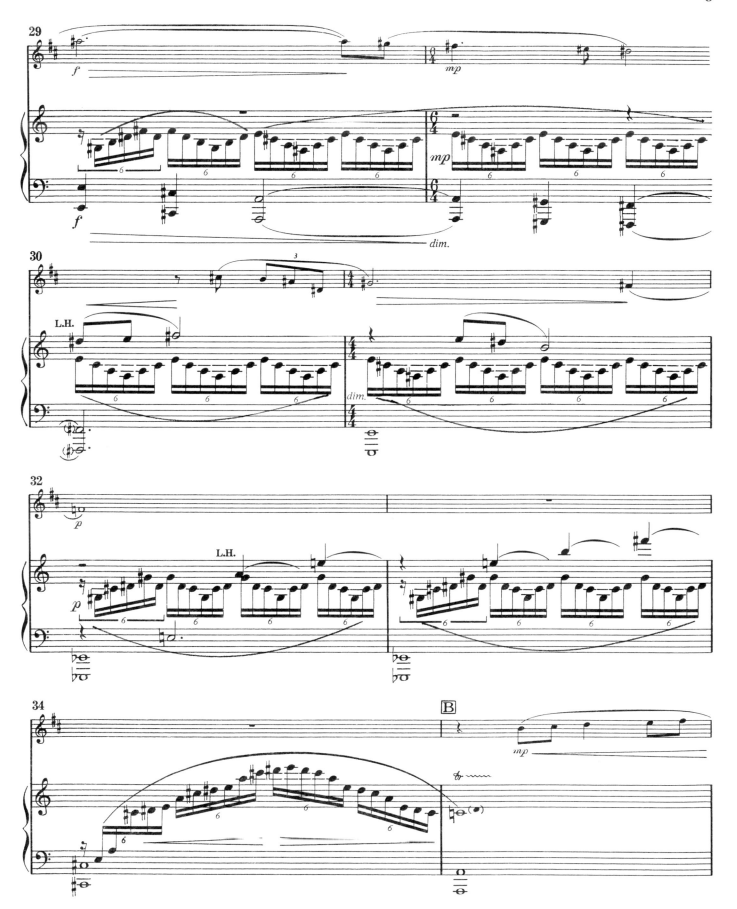

BrP TP190   *Photocopying is illegal - photocopier est illégal - Photokopieren ist rechtswidrig*

4

Photocopying is illegal - photocopier est illégal - Photokopieren ist rechtswidrig

5

6

Photocopying is illegal - photocopier est illégal - Photokopieren ist rechtswidrig

8

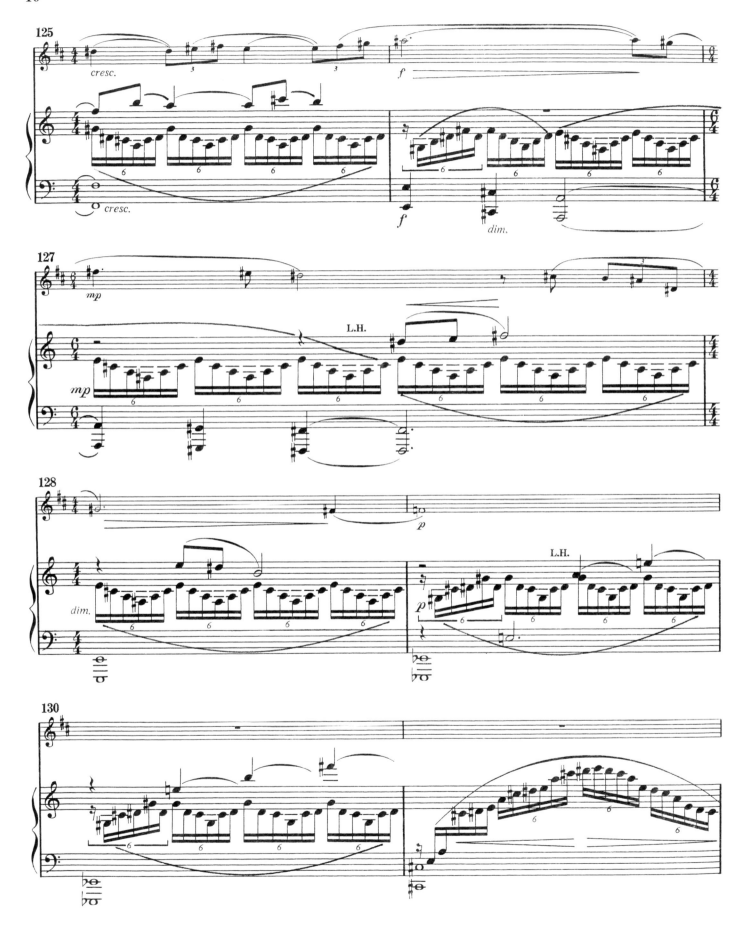

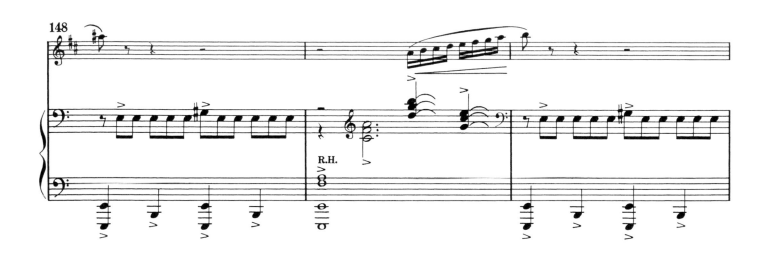

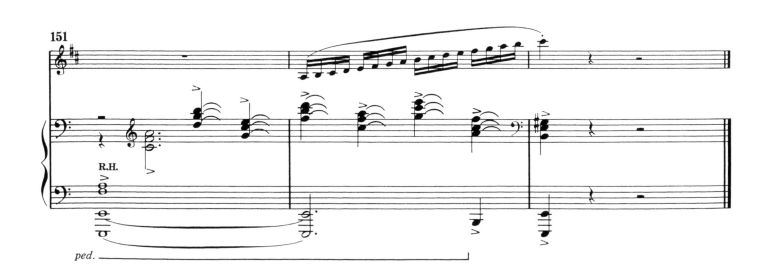

● METHODS & STUDIES FOR TRUMPET

BACH J.S. (1685-1750)

TP125   **12 Etudes** (from Goldberg Variations) (diff. 6) arr. John F. Sawyer

TP124   **24 Studies** (diff. 5-6) arr. by Stephen L. Glover

BENDINELLI Cesare (1542?-1617)

TP301   **Tutta l'Arte della Trombetta** (1614) - facsimile

TP302e   - E. H. Tarr: Translation, biography, critical comment

TP302d   - E. H. Tarr: Übersetzung, Biographie, kritischer Kommentar

TP302f   - E. H. Tarr Traduction, biographie, commentaire critique

BENTERFA Maurice (*1937)

TP51b   **Ort der Schwingungen - The Vibration Zone** + Japanese translation (all brass) diff. 1-4

TP51a   **Site des Vibrations - La Zona delle Vibrazioni - El Punto de Vibración** (Fr / It / Es) (all brass) (diff.1-4)

CONCONE Giuseppe (1801-1861)

TP138   **Lyrical Studies** trumpet (+ MP3) diff. 3-4 (ed. J.F.Sawyer)

DAVIDSON Louis (1912-1999)

TP7   **Techniques de la Trompette / Techniken des Trompetenspiels** (français / Deutsch) (diff. 2-5)

DION Jean-François (*1949)

TP348   **La Trompette Française** 15 portraits musicaux pour trompette (2015 - diff. 5-6)

FANTINI Girolamo (16??-16??)

TP140   **Modo per imparare a sonare** (1638) facsimile

TP187e   - Translation, biography, critical comment by E. H. Tarr

TP187d   - Übersetzung, Biographie, kritischer Kommentar E. H. Tarr

TP187f   - Traduction, biographie, commentaire critique par E. H. Tarr

FAVRE Pascal (*1949)

TP12   **Memento** (diff. 1-3)

FRIEDMAN Stanley (*1951)

TP95   **4 Etudes** (1996) trumpet or horn (diff. 4)

TP268   **Variations on a Limited Pitch Field** - 6 Concert Etudes (2004) for trumpet (diff. 4-5)

GIMENO José Antonio (1928-2017)

TP234   **12 Dodecaphonic Studies** (1961 - diff. 6)

LEWARK Egbert (*1953)

TP266   **Brass Circle** 38 Studies & Duets (diff. 3-5)

MACALUSO Rosario (*1956)

TP83   **7 Etudes de style** (diff. 4)

MASE Raymond (*1951)

TP327   **Extended Flexibility** (diff. 3-6) for trumpet & other valved brass instruments

NAVARRO Fats (1923-1950)

TP26   **Trumpet Chorus Book** (diff. 4 5) edited by Charlie Shoemake

PLOG Anthony (*1947)

TP53   **Etudes & Duets** Book I (diff. 1-2 - Bim Junior Series)

PRENTISS Henry H.

TP189   **Complete Preceptor, for the Cornopean, Bugle Horn & Key's Bugle**

QUINQUE Rolf (*1927)

TP10   **ASA-Jazz** (diff. 4-5)

TP11   **ASA Know How** (diff.3-5)

TP3   **ASA-Methode** (diff.1-6)

TP6   **ASA-Technik** (diff. 3-5)

RESKIN Charles (*1946)

TP269   **Advanced Trumpet Outings - Book 1** 16 Etudes & 13 Duets (2007 - diff. 4-5)

TP311   **Advanced Trumpet Outings Book 2** 14 Etudes & 14 Duets - (2011 - diff. 4-5)

TP319   **Easy Trumpet Outings** (Bim Junior Series) 12 Etudes & 11 Duets - (2011 - diff. 3) + MP3 acc.omp.

TP320   **Intermediate Trumpet Outings** (Bim Junior Series) 12 Etudes & 12 Duets - (2011 - diff. 3-4) + MP3 acc.omp.

ROY C. Eugène (ca. 1790-1827)

TP276   **Méthode de Trompette sans clef et avec clefs (1624)** - facsimile reprint, biography, historical presentation (Dt./Fr./Engl). by Adrian von Steiger / HKB Historical Brass Series 1

SAMPSON David (*1951)

TP278   **Morning Pages** - 21 Etudes for Trumpet (2005/2007 - diff. 4-6)

SANDOVAL Arturo (*1949)

TP42   **Brass Playing Concepts** + 12 Original Studies (1991 - diff. 4-6)

STAMP James (1904-1985)

   Warm-ups + Studies

TP2   (Français / Deutsch /English)

TP2e   (español)

TP2i   (italiano)

TP2j   (japanese)

TP2b   accompaniment for trumpet in Bb - MP3-download

TP2c   accompaniment for trumpet in C - MP3-download

TP277   **Supplemental Studies** to the original Warm-ups + Studies, + CD (diff. 1- 4 - edited by Thomas Stevens)

STAMP James / WIENER Jean-Christophe

TP2w   **How to play J. Stamp's Warm-ups - Wie spielt man die Warm-ups von J. Stamp? - Comment jouer les Warm-ups de J. Stamp** (Français / Deutsch / English)

TP2wi   **Come suonare i "Warm-ups" di J. Stamp - Como tocar los Warm-ups de J. Stamp** (italiano / espanol)

STEVENS Thomas (*1938)

TP101   **48 Lyric Studies** based on the Vocalises of Concone and Bordogni (diff. 2-4)

TP317   **After Schlossberg** Trumpet Studies as Taught By Leading Members of The Schlossberg School (diff. 2-5)

TP1   **Changing Meter Studies** (diff. 3)

TP5   **Contemporary Interval Studies** (diff. 3-4)

THOMPSON James (*1949)

TP215   **Bandroom Buzzing** (for classroom) (2008 - diff. 1-3)

TP216   **The Buzzing Book** (+ 2 CD C/Bflat) (2001 - diff. 1-6)

TROGNÉE Emile Joseph (1868-1942)

TP13   **15 Grandes Etudes** (diff. 5 - ed. Anatoly Selianin)

TP15   **25 Etudes techniques** (diff. 4-5 - ed. Anatoly Selianin)

TP14   **30 Etudes mélodiques** (diff. 4 - ed. Anatoly Selianin)

TP46   **Etudes finales** (diff. 4-5 - ed. Anatoly Selianin)

VIZZUTTI Allen (*1952)

TP182   **Advanced Etudes** (1982 - diff. 5-6)

WEBSTER Gerald (*1944)

TP184   **Method for Piccolo Trumpet** Vol. 1 (diff. 4-6)

TP185   **Method for Piccolo Trumpet** Vol. 2 (diff. 5)

---

ask for complete catalog - demandez notre catalogue complet - verlangen Sie unseren Gesamtkatalog

email: order@editions-bim.com - www.editions-bim.com

♪ MUSIC FOR TRUMPET AND PIANO

extract from our catalog - extrait de notre catalogue - Auszug aus unserm Katalog

ADAMS Byron (*1955)
TP116a **Concerto** trumpet & piano (or & strings, TP116b/c)

ALBINONI Tommaso (1671-1750)
TP118 **Sonata No 11 (St. Marc)** for trumpet & piano

ARUTIUNIAN Alexander (1920-2012)
TP31a **Concert Scherzo** for trumpet & piano
or trumpet & brass band (ref. TP31b/c)
TP210a **Elegy** for trumpet and piano reduction
or trumpet & strings, score & parts (ref. TP210b/c)

BARATTO Paolo (1926-2008)
TP195a **Concertino nostalgico** for trumpet & piano
TP63a **Intrada giocosa** for trumpet & organ (piano)
TP99 **Introduction e allegretto giocoso** trumpet & piano
TP67a **O! Solis splendor** for trumpet & piano
TP68a **Poculum Regis** for trumpet & piano

BESANCON André (*1946)
TP258a **Philosolo** for solo trumpet & piano
or solo trumpet & brass octet (ref. TP258b/c)

BRAHMS Johannes (1833-1897)
TP134 **Andante** for trumpet & piano (arr. John F. Sawyer)

BRÄM Thüring (*1944))
TP337 **Small Change** for trumpet & piano

CHARRIERE Caroline (*1960)
TP316a **Concertino** for trumpet & piano
or trumpet & chamber orchestra (ref. TP316b/c)
or trumpet & wind ensemble (ref. TP316d/e)

CHITCHYAN Geghuni (*1929)
TP236 **Humoresque** for trumpet & piano

CHKOLNIK ILIA (*1963)
TP256 **Romance** for trumpet and piano
TP102a **Trumpet Concerto** for trumpet & piano reduction
or trumpet & orchestra (TP102b/c)

DAVIS David (*1954)
TP139 **Quotation** for trumpet & piano

KASSATTI Tadeusz (*1948)
TP205 **Espagnolade** for trumpet & piano
TU49a **Kino Concertino** for trumpet & piano
or trumpet & strings (ref. TU49b/c)

KINCAID Rachel (*1986)
TP264 **Loss** for trumpet & piano

KREUTZER Conradin (1780-1849)
TP27a **Variationen in G** for trumpet & piano (ed. E.H. Tarr)
or trumpet & chamber orchestra (ref. TP27b/c)

LANE Richard (1933-2004)
TP253 **Sonatina No. 1** for trumpet and piano
TP254 **Sonatina No. 2** for trumpet and piano
TP250a **Song** for cornet (trumpet) and piano
or cornet (trp) & strings (ref. TP250b/c)

LONGINOTTI Paolo (1913-1963)
TP8 **Scherzo Iberico** for trumpet & piano

MARCELLO Benedetto (1686-1739)
TP154 **Sonata** for trumpet & piano (arr. Stephen Glover)

MEYER-SELB Horst (1933-2004)
TP226 **5 Bagatelles virtuos** for trumpet and piano

MICHEL Jean-François (*1957)
TP324 **Don Quichotte** for trumpet (or cornet /flugelhorn) and piano
TP332 **Lorie** for trumpet (or cornet / flugelhorn) and piano
TP335 **Canto y Danza** (2004) for trumpet & piano
TP333 **Klezmeralda** (2012) for trumpet (or clarinet) & piano
TP326 **Promenades Musicales** (2013) for trumpet & piano
TP328 **Scaramouche** (2013) for trumpet & piano
TP331 **Why not?** (2011) for trumpet & piano

PLOG Anthony (*1947)
TP272a **Contemplation** (2007) for fluegelhorn & piano
or fluegelhorn & wind ensemble (ref. TP272b/c/d)
TP330 **Musings** (2014) for trumpet & piano
TP57a **Nocturne** (2010) for trumpet & piano
TP323 **Paradigms** (2012) for flugelhorn (trumpet) & piano
TP314 **Scherzo** (2011) for trumpet & piano
TP313 **Sonata** (2009) for trumpet & piano
TP351a **Trumpet Concerto No.3** (2015) for trumpet & piano
or trumpet & brass band (ref. TP351b/c)

PONCHIELLI Amilcare (1834-1886)
TP9a **Concerto per Tromba** for trumpet and piano
(or see also trumpet & strings, or and wind band)

RESKIN Charles (*1946)
TP350 **Chet the Jet** (2015) for trumpet & piano
TP289 **Sonata** (2007) for trumpet & piano
TP353 **Sonata** No. 2 (2016-2017) for trumpet & piano
TP338a **Passages** (2014) for trumpet & piano
(or Trumpet & chamber orchestra - ref. TP338b/c)

SACHSE (1813-1870)
TP167a **Concertino in Eb** (publ.1871) for trumpet (cornet) & piano
or cornet & brass ensemble (ed. S.Glover) (ref. TP167b/c)

SAGLIETTI Corrado Maria (*1957)
TP329 **Concertino per Tromba** for trumpet & piano

SHAKHOV Ilia E. (*1925)
TP173 **Scherzo** for trumpet & piano (ed. Steven Winick)

STEVENS, John (*1951)
TP296 **Autumn** for trumpet & piano
TP290 **Sonata** for trumpet & piano

TANAKA Karen (*1961)
TP249 **Silent Ocean** for Trumpet and piano

TROGNÉE Emile Joseph (1868-1942)
TP86 **Valse lente** for trumpet & piano (ed. Anatoly Selianin)

TSCHAIKOVSKY Piotr I. (1840-1893)
TP181a **Danse Napolitaine (Lac des Cygnes)** for trumpet & piano
(arrangement David Hickman)

TURRIN Joseph (*1947)
TP190 **Caprice** for trumpet & piano
TP202a **Elegy** for trumpet & piano reduction
or trumpet & strings (ref. TP202b/c)
TP255 **3 Episodes** for trumpet and piano
TP242 **In Memoriam** for trumpet & piano
TP201 **Intrada** for trumpet & piano
TP211 **Four Miniatures** for trumpet (flugelhorn) and piano
TP203 **2 Portraits** for flugelhorn (cornet or trumpet) & piano

---

ask for complete catalog - demandez notre catalogue complet - verlangen Sie unseren Gesamtkatalog

email: order@editions-bim.com - www.editions-bim.com